The Story of our Life

A GRANDPARENTS BOOK

WRITING YOUR BOOK

For some curious reason, we tend to underestimate the interest the story of our life holds for the younger members of our family. But to provide a brief account of one's memories is to give them something no-one else can give.

The bonds between grandparents and grandchildren are often very close. So much that seemed ordinary to the older generation when they were young is fascinating to a child growing up now, in a seemingly different world.

Not everyone is born to be an author, so this book has been developed to provide the prompts, and some type of structure, to encourage the writing of a simple life-story. It has been designed to be equally well suited to either a single grandparent or a couple (although each may prefer to have their own copy).

Depending on the age of the grandchild or grandchildren for whom it is intended, the compiling of the book could become a project for the two generations to undertake together, with the child asking the questions and then writing down the answers.

However you decide to use it, this book provides the means of handing down a parcel of history to the future generations of your family. If you can imagine what interest your great grandparents' description of their early life would have held for you as a child, you will understand the fascination your story will hold for your grandchildren, their children and succeeding generations.

CONTENTS

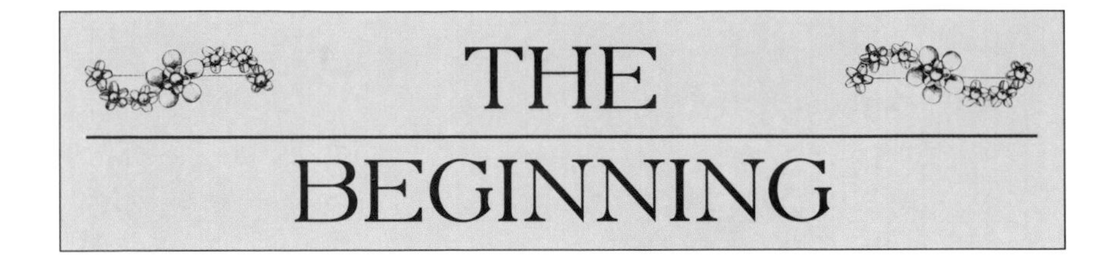

THE BEGINNING

What is your full name?

When and where were you born?

How much did you weigh at birth?

How old were your parents when you were born?

Why were you given your first names?

PHOTOGRAPH

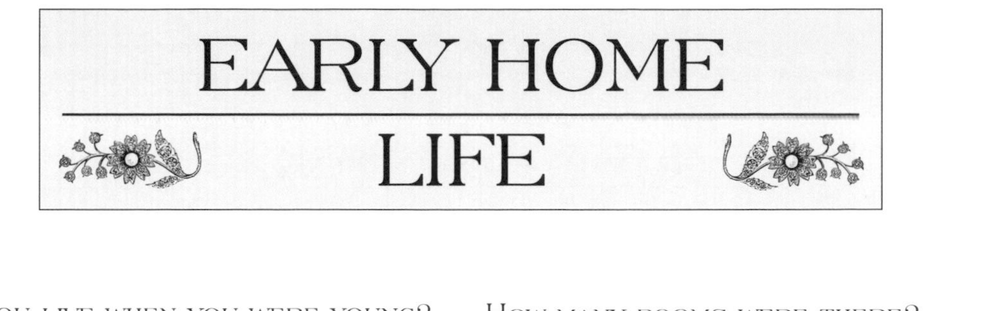

EARLY HOME LIFE

WHERE DID YOU LIVE WHEN YOU WERE YOUNG?

WHAT DO YOU REMEMBER ABOUT IT?

WHAT SORT OF BUILDING WAS IT? DID IT HAVE A GARDEN?

HOW MANY ROOMS WERE THERE?

DID YOU HAVE A ROOM OF YOUR OWN?

DID YOU MOVE HOME WHEN YOU WERE YOUNG?

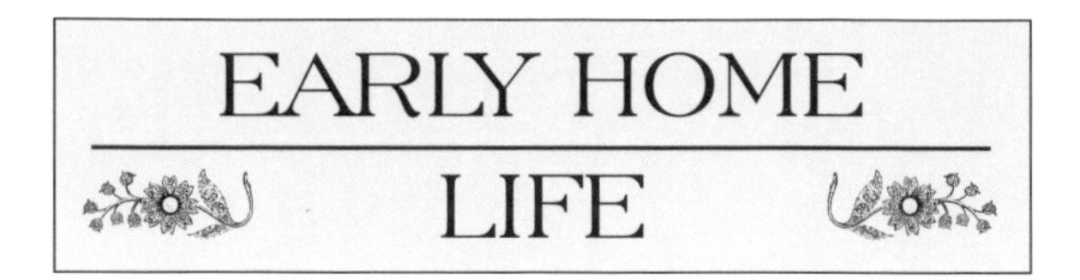

EARLY HOME LIFE

What are your earliest memories?

Did you have any special toys?

What games did you play at home?

Did you have any hobbies?

Did you have a bicycle?

How old were you when you learned to ride it?

Tenement Mother and Children

Marie Page (1914)

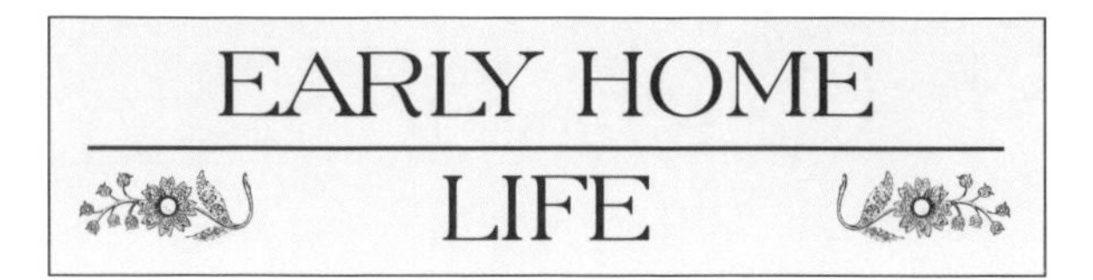

EARLY HOME LIFE

Did you receive regular pocket money? From what age? Did you have to earn it?

How much did you receive and what did you spend it on?

Can you remember the prices of any of the things you used to buy?

ITEM	PRICE

EARLY HOME LIFE

DID YOU HAVE PARTIES ON YOUR BIRTHDAY?

DO YOU HAVE ANY MEMORIES OF CHRISTMAS DAY WHEN YOU WERE YOUNG?

WHAT OTHER MEMORIES DO YOU HAVE OF YOUR EARLY FAMILY LIFE?

YOUR FATHER

WHAT WAS YOUR FATHER'S NAME AND DATE OF BIRTH AND WHERE WAS HE BORN?

PLEASE DESCRIBE HIS APPEARANCE. WHAT WAS HIS OCCUPATION?

WHAT WERE HIS OTHER INTERESTS AND HOBBIES?

WHAT ARE YOUR FONDEST MEMORIES OF HIM?

PHOTOGRAPH

YOUR MOTHER

What was your mother's maiden name?

What was her date of birth and where was she born?

Please describe her appearance. What were her special interests and talents?

What was her occupation before her marriage?

What are your fondest memories of her?

PHOTOGRAPH

YOUR FATHER'S PARENTS

What were their names? When and where were they born? What were their occupations? How old were they when they died?

YOUR FATHER'S FATHER

YOUR FATHER'S MOTHER

PHOTOGRAPH

Eugene Manet with his Daughter at Bougival, c.1881
BERTHE MORISOT (1841–1895)

YOUR MOTHER'S PARENTS

WHAT WERE THEIR NAMES? WHEN AND WHERE WERE THEY BORN? WHAT WERE THEIR OCCUPATIONS? HOW OLD WERE THEY WHEN THEY DIED?

YOUR MOTHER'S FATHER

YOUR MOTHER'S MOTHER

PHOTOGRAPH

YOUR BROTHERS & SISTERS

WHAT WERE THE NAMES OF YOUR BROTHERS AND SISTERS? WHEN AND WHERE WERE THEY BORN?

NAME	DATE AND TIME	PLACE

WHAT DO YOU PARTICULARLY REMEMBER ABOUT THEM FROM YOUR CHILDHOOD?

WHAT WERE THEIR OCCUPATIONS AS ADULTS?

WHAT ARE YOUR FONDEST MEMORIES OF EACH OF THEM IN ADULT LIFE?

PHOTOGRAPH

SCHOOLDAYS

PLEASE DESCRIBE YOUR FIRST SCHOOL. HOW OLD WERE YOU WHEN YOU FIRST WENT THERE? WHAT DO YOU REMEMBER ABOUT THE PLACE AND THE TEACHERS?

WHICH SCHOOL DID YOU MOVE ON TO AFTER THAT?

HOW DID YOU TRAVEL TO SCHOOL?

SCHOOLDAYS

What did you most enjoy about going to school? At which subjects did you do best?

How much homework were you given?

Were there any subjects you disliked?

Did you ever get into trouble at school? What happened?

School is Out, 1889

ELIZABETH STANHOPE FORBES (1859-1912)

SCHOOLDAYS

Did you enjoy music and singing? Did you learn to play any musical instruments? Can you still play any?

Were you good at sports? Which ones did you play?

Did you have a part-time paid job while still in school? How much did you earn?

FURTHER EDUCATION

How old were you when you left school?

Did you know what you wanted to do in life?

Did you go on to further studies?

Where did you go and what did you study?

WHY DID YOU CHOOSE THIS SUBJECT? DID YOU GAIN ANY QUALIFICATIONS?

DID YOU MAKE ANY NEW FRIENDS DURING THIS TIME?

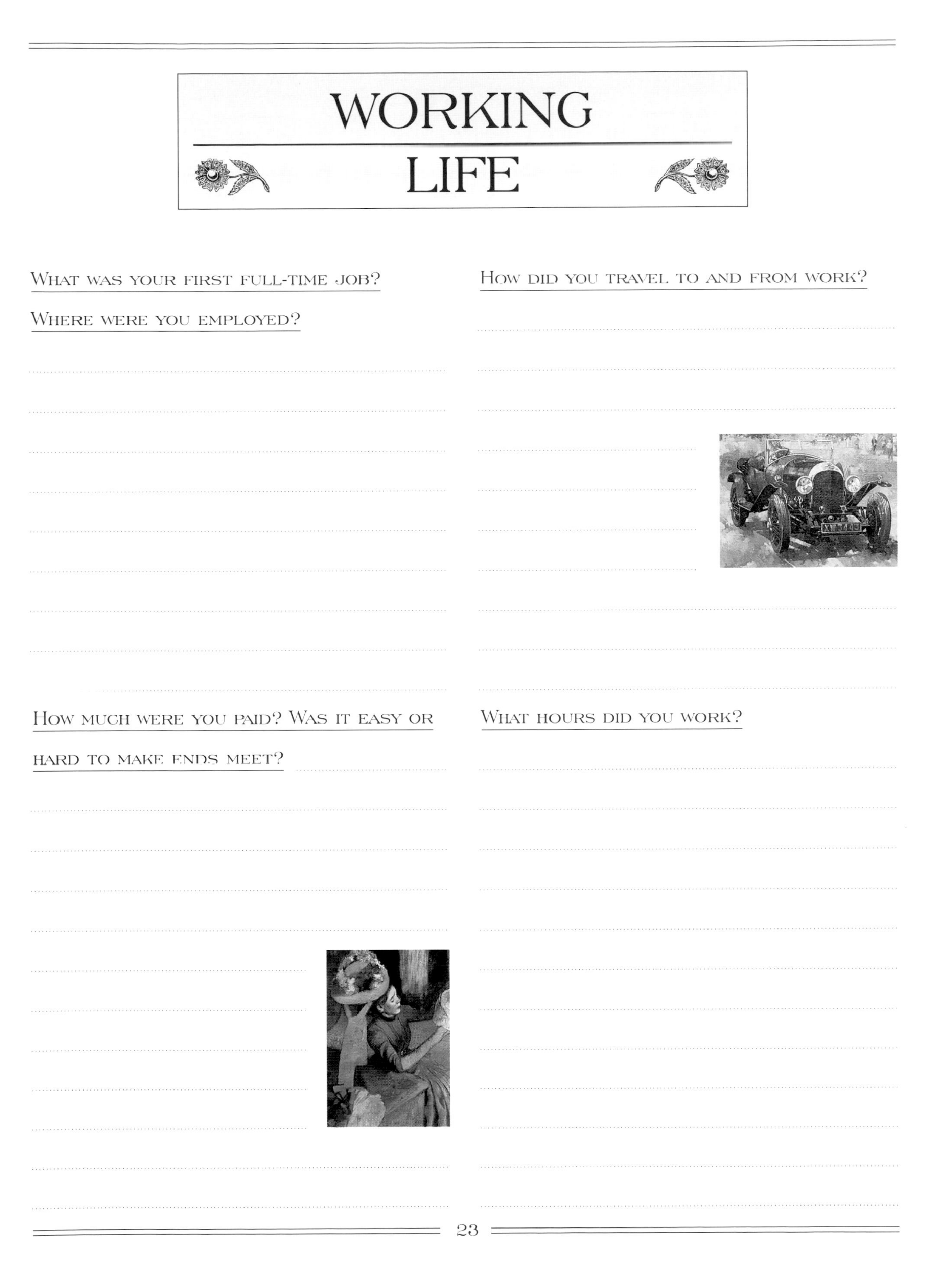

WORKING LIFE

WHAT WAS YOUR FIRST FULL-TIME JOB?

WHERE WERE YOU EMPLOYED?

HOW DID YOU TRAVEL TO AND FROM WORK?

HOW MUCH WERE YOU PAID? WAS IT EASY OR HARD TO MAKE ENDS MEET?

WHAT HOURS DID YOU WORK?

WORKING LIFE

How long did you stay in your first job?

What was your main occupation during your working life?

Did you find your work fulfilling?

Have you ever done any voluntary or charity work?

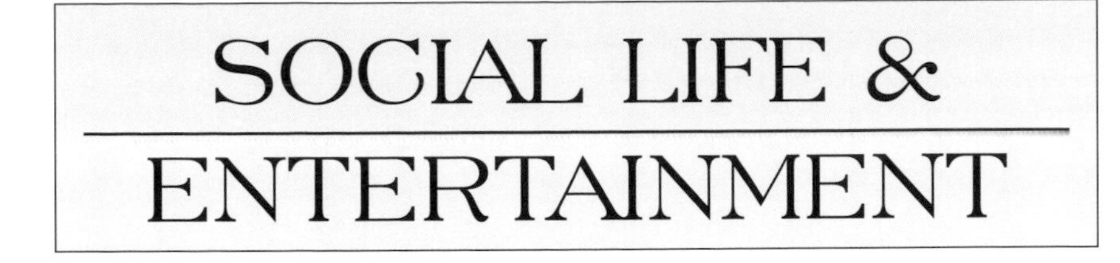

SOCIAL LIFE & ENTERTAINMENT

Can you remember the first clothes you bought with your own money?

How did you usually travel when you were a teenager?

What sort of entertainment did you enjoy most? Can you remember any particularly enjoyable times?

Who was your favourite singer? Actor? Actress?

When did you go on your first date? Who was it with and where did you go?

Were there any places that you used to go out to regularly in the evenings?

Danse à la Ville

Pierre-Auguste Renoir (1841-1919)

WHEN YOU MET

How did you first meet? How old were you? What were you both doing at that time?

What were your first impressions of each other?

WHEN YOU MET

How long did you go out together before you became engaged?

Were you still living with your parents?

How did your parents greet the news of your engagement?

How long was your engagement?

YOUR WEDDING

WHAT WAS THE DATE OF YOUR WEDDING?

HOW OLD WERE YOU WHEN YOU MARRIED?

WHERE DID THE CEREMONY TAKE PLACE?

WHAT DID YOU WEAR ON YOUR WEDDING DAY?

WHO WAS YOUR BEST MAN? WHO WAS YOUR BRIDESMAID?

HOW MANY GUESTS CAME? DID YOU HAVE A RECEPTION? WHERE WAS IT HELD?

The Wedding Morning, 1892
John Henry Frederick Bacon (1866–1913)

YOUR WEDDING

What are your chief memories of that day?

Do you still have any presents you received?

Did you go away on honeymoon?

PHOTOGRAPH

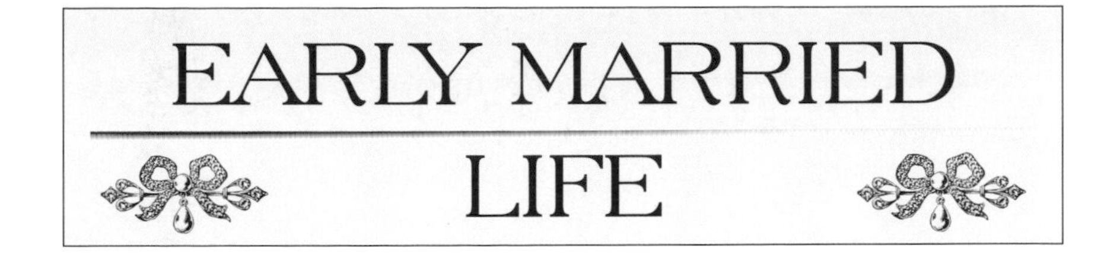

EARLY MARRIED LIFE

Where was your first home together? Can you describe it?

Why did you choose to live where you did?

Did you ever go back there later? What were your impressions then?

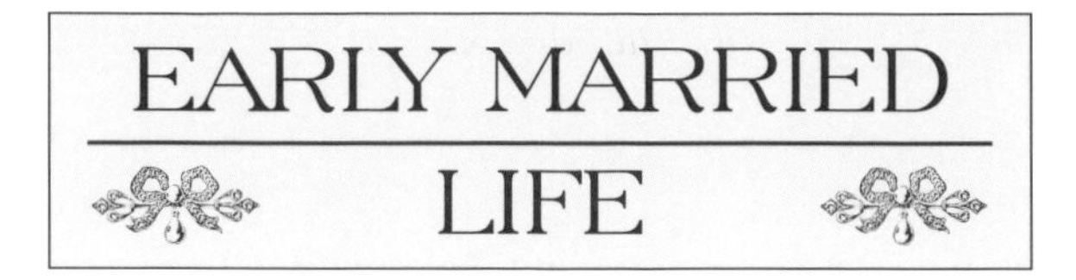

What were your children's names? When and where were they born? Do you remember how much they weighed at birth?

NAME	DATE AND TIME	PLACE	WEIGHT

Where did your children go to school?

What were their best subjects?

Mother and Child
Mary Cassatt (1844-1926)

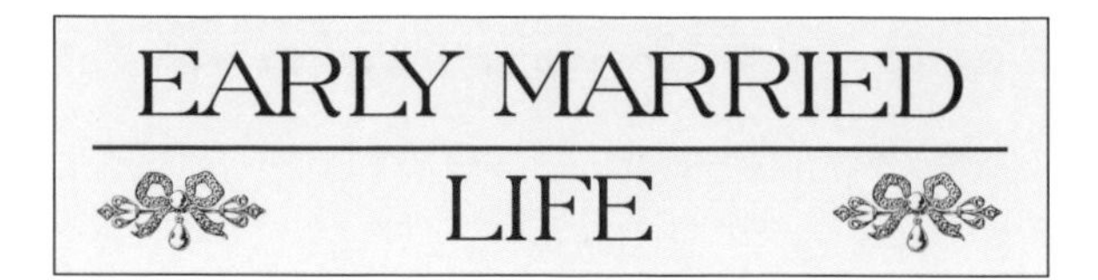

EARLY MARRIED LIFE

What was your monthly income in the early years of your marriage?

Did it sometimes seem hard to make ends meet?

Can you remember the prices of some of the things you used to buy regularly?

ITEM	PRICE THEN	PRICE NOW

What did you do in your leisure hours?

What are your happiest memories of those early days?

PHOTOGRAPH

BEST FRIENDS

WHO HAVE BEEN YOUR BEST FRIENDS DURING YOUR LIFE?

HOW DID YOU MEET THEM AND GET TO KNOW THEM?

ARE THEY SIMILAR IN CHARACTER TO YOU? WHY DO YOU THINK YOU HAVE GOT ON SO WELL?

Boating Scene at Maidenhead
SIR JOHN LAVERY (1856–1941)

BEST FRIENDS

WHAT IS THE SINGLE MOST IMPORTANT THING THAT YOU HAVE SHARED WITH EACH OF THEM?

WHAT IS THE HAPPIEST MEMORY YOU HAVE OF EACH OF THEM?

WHAT ARE THEY DOING NOW?

PHOTOGRAPH

THE CARS YOU HAVE OWNED

CAN YOU RECALL ALL THE DIFFERENT CARS YOU HAVE OWNED, AND WHAT YOU PAID FOR THEM?

MAKE AND MODEL	YEAR BOUGHT	PRICE PAID

WHICH DID YOU ENJOY THE MOST? WHY?

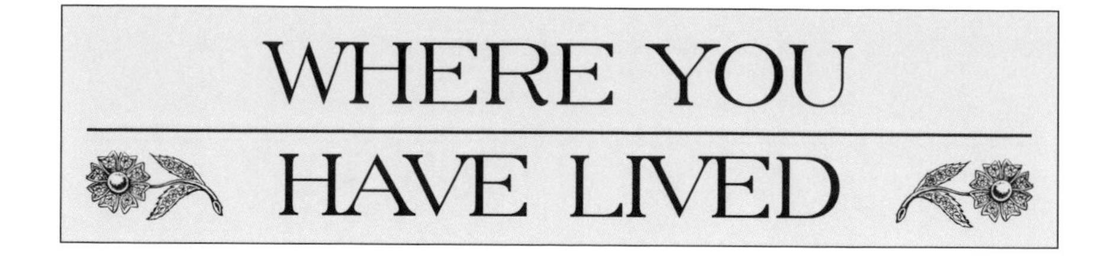

WHERE YOU HAVE LIVED

Can you remember all the places in which you have lived during your life? Do you know how much (either to rent or to buy) was paid for them?

DATE	ADDRESS	TYPE OF PROPERTY	COST

If you had to live in only one of these, which one would you choose, and why?

YOUR HOLIDAYS

Can you remember any of your holidays when you were a child? What sort of holiday did you most enjoy then?

Did you go anywhere particularly interesting or exciting after you left school and before you married?

PHOTOGRAPH

YOUR HOLIDAYS

Where did you go on holiday when your children were young?

What type of holiday do you enjoy most now?

Which country would you most like to visit? Why would you like to go there?

Children Playing by the Seashore
DOROTHEA SHARP (1874-1955)

IMPORTANT EVENTS

HAVE YOU EVER MET ANY FAMOUS PEOPLE?

WHAT WERE THE CIRCUMSTANCES?

HAVE YOU PERSONALLY WITNESSED ANY EXCITING OR SIGNIFICANT HISTORICAL EVENTS?

AND...

What is the one thing you would like to do during the next twelve months?

What has given you the most happiness in your life?

What is the most exciting thing that has ever happened to you?

AND...

WHAT IS THE FUNNIEST THING THAT HAS EVER HAPPENED TO YOU?

WHAT IS THE BEST PIECE OF ADVICE YOU EVER RECEIVED?

IF YOU COULD CHOOSE AN OCCUPATION FOR A SINGLE DAY, WHAT WOULD YOU CHOOSE; AND WHY?

This book was completed on